First published in 2015 by

The Solopreneur Publishing Company Ltd

Cedars Business Centre, Barnsley Road, Hemsworth, West Yorkshire WF9 4PU

www.thesolopreneur.co.uk

Printed in the U.K.

For further copies, please go to - www.oodlebooks.com, theblinks.co.uk and Amazon. Also available on Kindle.

Dedication

To the world's Carers.

Caring helps children and young people lock away love inside them.

Keep up the good work.

Andrea Chatten Msc, MBPsS, PGCL&M, Bed(Hons), Dip.CBT

Andrea has been a specialised teacher for over 25 years, working with children from ages 5-16 with emotional and behavioural difficulties. She is currently working as 'Lead Children's Emotional & Behavioural Psychologist' at Unravel CEBPC primarily with schools and families in and around the Sheffield area.

Developing positive, trusting relationships has always been at the heart of her practice with children and young people to nudge them into improved psychological well-being. Over the years, Andrea has developed and applied many positive developmental psychology approaches.

This insight is incorporated into her stories, in order to help children, young people, and their families to gain more of an understanding and potential strategies to try to deal with a range of behavioural issues that children and young people could experience.

Andrea created "The Blinks" so that parents and carers could also benefit from reading the books with their children, particularly if they can identify with the children in the stories, and their own family circumstances. Both parent or carer and child could learn how to manage early forms of psychological distress as a natural part of growing up, rather than it become problematic when not addressed in its early stages.

'The Blinks' is a series of books that discreetly apply lots of psychological theory throughout the stories, including Cognitive Behavioural Therapy, Developmental and Positive Psychology approaches.

This book in the series tackles the issue of anger and how to prevent this everyday cognition from becoming a more serious anxiety in the future.

Introduction

'The Blinks' books have been created to help children, young people and their families understand the feelings that can underpin emotional and behavioural issues. With greater insight into emotions, the strategies and techniques provided in this book can help manage and change the intensity and duration of problematic behaviours over time.

The second Blinks' book 'Anger' follows the story of Robbie, whose life hasn't always been great, particularly during the last few years. One day, and on possibly the worst day of his life, it all gets too much for him and his anger explodes! The choices that Robbie makes throughout the story and the ways in which he deals with his angry feelings adds to the day, making it go from bad to worse.

It is important to remember that anger is a perfectly normal emotion that has, most likely, been part of our brain function across human evolution. What Robbie initially feels is totally understandable. Anger is not a *bad* emotion, but a lot of the time it is regarded as such due to how it can be used and displayed. In fact, anger is hugely important in helping us deal with difficult situations that could leave us feeling hurt or threatened. The problems begin to arise when our control of the angry feelings weaken, which can lead us to do 'bad' things in the heat of the moment, which contributes further to the negative label that anger can hold.

In this story Robbie's anger is beginning to become problematic due to the negative impact it is having on his everyday life including his relationships (at home and at school), the quality of his learning, his anger becoming aggressive, and also it being taken out on other people. All of these factors slowly chip away at Robbie's self-confidence and self-esteem, leading him to feel that he is a bad person because he does bad things when he is hurting inside.

As the story develops Robbie learns to understand his negative feelings with the help of Chika Change-Your-Thoughts and he learns some valuable tools to try to help him regain control of this intense and, at times, difficult emotion.

Remember: this combination of insight + action is fundamental to positive behaviour change.

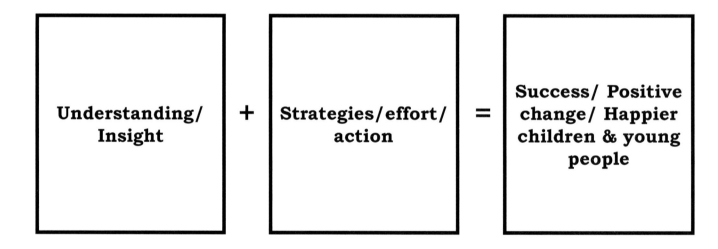

This book aims to help you, as the active adult in a child or young person's life, to understand the theory behind The Blinks' interventions that are used to support Robbie with his anger. The more empowered you are about your understanding of difficult feelings, the more confident you will be to guide and nudge the children and young people in your care towards improved emotional understanding and self-management.

Section 1 - <u>The Psychology of Anger.</u>

As humans, we are programmed to feel. These feelings are essential to us engaging with life and making the right choices but, more importantly, if they are listened to correctly they can play an essential role in informing us that something might not be as it should. It is these complex feelings, triggered by either positive or negative experiences, which dictate our behavioural responses.

Anger can be one of our most useful emotions. It not only alerts us to potential dangers, but can also be a brilliant motivator for us to do things differently so that we re-establish security and protection for ourselves and for our loved ones. It can also be powerful for inciting change for the better, as our history books and newspapers reflect. Important uses for anger:

- It kicks in adrenaline, which gives us power to sort out a problem head on if we need to, or run like the wind if we are in danger (fight or flight)
- It helps to reduce intense underlying difficult feelings. Anger never exists alone, it is always underpinned by other powerful feelings such as sadness, grief, feelings of failure, hurt, shame or jealousy
- It lets others know how we are feeling or if they have upset us without us needing to open our mouths!

It is important to remember here that all emotions are valid and exist for a reason. We can't expect to feel happy or capable if we deny our difficult feelings for too long.

Acknowledging a feeling allows the brain to turn down the volume of that particular emotion. This is important as each feeling has a purpose and needs to be listened to. Learning how to recognise and manage our emotions is crucial to feelings of well-being and resilience.

The problem with anger is that it can, at times, be expressed very negatively which labels it as a potentially harmful emotion. It is important to remember that anger is not 'bad', it is what we do with it that makes it so. If anger is beginning to be expressed frequently and is not controlled positively, then it can become a problem. Anger could be seen to be problematic when:

- It becomes aggressive and results in violence
- It begins to affect your quality of life
- It causes problems in your relationships
- It is used as a form of control
- It is internalised rather than expressed positively

It is important to note that children learn about anger and other emotions from you, the active adult in their life. As parents, we hope that children will learn more from what we say than what we do. However, in reality, our modelling of emotions is the most powerful lesson children will ever learn.

If, as adults, we manage our emotions negatively, then those styles can become learned behaviour for our children. That doesn't mean that we shouldn't get angry, as we wouldn't be human if life didn't make us feel cross at times. Nevertheless, it is hugely important that we express our feelings with control, explanation and reflection.

Children whose parents do not display emotions leave their children struggling to name uncomfortable feelings, never mind knowing what to do with them for the better. Many of us do, at times, try to hide difficult emotions or try to ignore them, but this doesn't stop them from being there. Burying negative feelings inside can hinder children from understanding emotions by depriving them of the opportunity to explore the best possible outcomes which, over time, can impact upon on their ability to control feelings and actions across their lifespan, which can affect long-term well-being.

As parents, it is essential that we teach and guide our children and young people through the difficulties life can present. Emotions can't be switched on and off, as they arise from experiences. It is at this time that we need to support them in recognising what they feel, facing it head on, feeling it, accepting it is there for a reason and then knowing what to do with it, so that it doesn't become a problem.

Types of Anger

Angry behaviours can present in many forms including:

Aggressive – This form of anger can have huge negative consequences for children, young people and those around them. It can include hitting, punching, kicking, throwing things, threatening, swearing or verbal abuse.

Transferred – Sometimes, anger can be directed onto other people rather than being expressed towards the people who have actually triggered the angry feelings in the first place. Sometimes, your child may transfer angry feelings from an incident at school onto you when they come home. Children and young people need to learn how to manage anger in the situations that may have triggered it, in order to change the situation for the better at that moment and in the future.

Suppressed – This type of anger can have damaging effects on emotional and physical well-being. By not being honest about our feelings and trying to bury them deep down inside us, they can eventually erupt and be incredibly destructive. This form of anger can lead to children and young people seeing themselves as bad people due to the extreme responses that sometimes occur when they are actually feeling at their most vulnerable.

Internalised – When anger is negatively directed inside us, it can be incredibly damaging. This can lead to children and young people become overly critical about themselves, and in more extreme cases begin to self-injure as a form of emotional coping through distraction and avoidance.

It is important to highlight here that people, situations and events are not responsible for making our children angry, they only trigger angry feelings. Everybody on the planet will have a complex series of emotional, physiological or psychological triggers which are more likely to activate angry feelings. Yet it is important that we as adults teach our children that they are in charge of how angry they become, not the other person involved or the situation at the time.

Psychological triggers that can accelerate angry feelings include:

- Physiological factors, such as being ill, tired, hungry, wet or cold
- Emotional factors such as stress, grief, states of anxiety
- Work, school and relationship issues
- Learned behavioural responses about anger
- Social conditioning – how productive your anger is at getting you what you want – either now or in the past
- Internal belief mechanisms

From this list, we can see that, should any of the above be challenged, under threat or violated, then our anger responses could be awakened. It is at these times that we need to keep our rational brain active, whenever possible, in order to maintain levels of control and support, appropriate to desired outcomes. At this time, our internal dialogue helps or hinders our ability to self-regulate. This will be discussed in greater detail in section 2 and how Cognitive Behavioural Therapy can support anger.

How Anger affects behavioural changes

When our bodies feel in danger or threatened in any way, our brains kick into action to activate the necessary responses for us to fundamentally survive. Rational thought occurs in the pre-frontal cortex or frontal lobe area of the brain which is responsible for thinking and making decisions. When our brain perceives danger then our more primitive brain awakens and responds automatically. This is the same quick reaction that our brain has been using since our caveman days.

If, all those millions of years ago, as we were out hunting for food, we were suddenly faced with an unexpected woolly mammoth, our brain would be alerted to either run as fast as we can or fight for our life with whatever weapon we possessed. This is where anger gets its power. The adrenal glands, which sit snuggly on top of the kidneys, are ordered to release adrenaline which surges us with energy. This strength assists us in doing what is needed, so that we are not in prolonged danger and can escape as best as possible. Our body is also flooded with other chemicals including cortisol, the stress hormone, and oxygen to fuel us further.

At this time, our bodies also begin to work differently which contributes further to the behavioural changes that will occur. We tend to breathe in shorter and faster breaths, to slow down the amount of oxygen being used, so that it can go to our muscles should they need it. This increased oxygen also causes the heart to beat faster, thus getting oxygen into the bloodstream and to where it is needed as quickly as possible. Increased blood flow to muscles and the powerful hormones that have been produced, make our bodies feel tight and strong and ready for action. Other physiological changes include:

- Red face due to increased blood movement

- Dry mouth or throat

- Knot in our stomach due to intense sense of emotions

- Quick or louder speech to scare off the potential danger

- Feeling sick due to the digestive system shutting down, so the fuel used to support digestion gets used elsewhere

- Tears. This relieves stress and helps the body calm down and regain control

- Inability to keep still or shaking due to the muscles being powered by adrenaline

- An urge to hurt someone. This is never the best option as it will always lead to greater problems. Children struggle to recover from these acts when young which affects positive self-esteem or more worryingly, over time, can become desensitised to violence which interferes hugely with the development of moral understanding.

As you can see, these evolutionary mechanisms hi-jack all other brain activity. They are even thought to reduce intelligence by roughly 30%, due to the rational thinking part of the brain not working as effectively. This is when our brain definitely isn't our friend. Just because it suggests something, doesn't mean that it is the best idea!

Our role in helping children and young people understand anger is helping them to learn as many positive strategies that work for them and to keep the thinking brain functional at this time. This takes time, trial and error and reflection to develop the desired skills. More importantly it needs opportunities for children and young people to feel and be angry so that the appropriate learning can occur.

This explains why at times of heightened emotional distress we could feel out of control, and to a certain extent we are. Out instinctive and impulsive brain has taken over, steering us to what can sometimes be reckless outcomes. These behaviours can be what makes anger the problematic emotion.

Top tips for supporting angry feelings

- Help children name what they are feeling from an early age and let them know that whatever they are feeling is ok. You can teach them ways to manage it so that they won't hurt themselves or others

- Help children understand their triggers. They might be particularly sensitive to certain things more than others. Knowing our triggers puts us in charge of our emotions and provides greater understanding

- Teach reflection so that they can decide on the person that they want to become

- Use breathing to get back in control. Slower and deeper breathing floods the brain with oxygen which releases calming chemicals. This process reduces angry feelings and our intelligent thinking kicks back in

- Try it and see. Give children as many options as possible to see what works best for them. They then have their own anger tool kit for whenever it is needed

- Count to 10, 100, 1000! This gives them time for their angry feelings to ease. It also activates their smarter brain by having to focus on something else and distracts their dialogue from negative self-talk

- Do exercise, go for a walk. This gives their brain the time to get things under control and get away from the situation that may have triggered the anger

- Suggest that children tell the person what they did to make them angry. If they are still angry when they do this, people will only hear their aggression and not the message behind it, which is the most important

- Let the angry energy out! Punch a pillow, try to rip a magazine, telephone directory, stomp around, anything that is safe and won't hurt them or others

- Talk to people. This helps with reflection and seeing what worked and what didn't work this time so they are more prepared for what to do next time

- Scream loudly. This turns emotional distress into a physical expression and moves the anger onwards

- Give children the freedom to cry. This releases stress which will make them feel drained and tired. Let them sleep if they can. Things nearly always feel better when they wake up

- Help children and young people to write things down. Expressing their anger at a person or situation in words can help hugely. It is the process of getting the angry feelings out. They are allowed to think whatever they think; they are their thoughts and their feelings. That way they don't need to hurt others when they are angry, they don't always need to know what they felt which puts us in charge of our emotions

Questions for discussion with children and young people

1. Have you ever felt like Robbie?

2. What do you do when you feel angry?

3. Write a list of things that make you angry. This could be people, situations, places, negative attitudes.

4. Who do you think is in charge of your anger? Why?

5. Draw a volcano. Using your list of things that make you angry, write them in lava streams coming out of the volcano. Then draw rain clouds floating above and write down things that you could do to cool the angry lava.

6. If you were Blink Chika Change-Your-Thoughts, what advice would you give Robbie?

Section 2 – <u>Cognitive Behavourial Therapy (CBT) approaches to support anger management</u>

Cognitive psychology is concerned with the mental processes of learning and gaining understanding through experience, how we process our thoughts and feelings through senses. CBT is a psychological approach which can help us recognise how thoughts affect how we feel and fundamentally what we believe. The main principles of CBT are based on two main factors:

1. If we think something for long enough, we will eventually feel it.
2. The longer we feel it, the more likely we are to believe it.

Robbie's negative thinking throughout the story fuels his anger further and further until it explodes. Before he started working with Chika Change-Your-Thoughts, Robbie had no skills or tools to try to reduce his anger once it had become triggered. His negative thoughts fuel angry feelings until they take over and Robbie loses control. Luckily Chika Change-Your-Thoughts helps him to know what to do at difficult times and how not to feel so disappointed with himself afterwards.

Feelings are not always facts!

The important component of CBT and Positive Psychology is recognising how our thoughts affect how we feel and in turn what we believe about ourselves and the world in which we live. The diagram below helps us to understand how each phase feeds into the next.

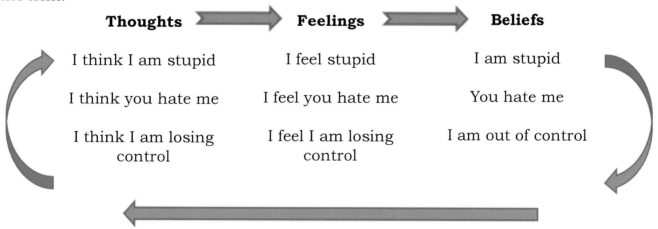

We would all like to believe that our brain is right all of the time and that when it suggests something, then it must be the right decision for that time. Sadly this is not always the case. Our brain is not always our best friend, especially in emotional situations.

We need to help our children recognise that just because our brain churns out possibilities, this does not mean that they are always the wisest. We need to challenge the choices that our brain is offering so that we make the best one which, sometimes for all of us, is not always easy. One thing that we can take comfort from is that the brain is not expecting us to make the absolutely best choice ever; it simply needs one that is good enough.

It is also important for us to realise that these negative thoughts and the amount of attention that we give to them, can have a devastating impact on how we feel in day to day situations. Before we know it, small things can escalate into much bigger issues. Nevertheless, the brain is an awesome human feature and with understanding and practice, we can change things for the better and develop newer healthier brain pathways and circuits.

<u>Bias thinking patterns (errors in thinking rationally)</u>

As children, young people and adults, we can be affected by negative thoughts that can fool us and so we are more likely to respond with automatic behaviours. We can also believe that we know what the other person is thinking and this, we feel, is mostly being directed negatively towards us. By understanding that we do this can help to make us feel empowered, but also more effective in challenging irrational thoughts. Throughout the story, Robbie is negatively affected with many bias thinking patterns which steer his negative behaviour choices. Some examples are:

Mind reading

As a child, young person or adult, we can believe that we know what the other person is thinking and this is mostly being directed towards us. Although our brains are brilliant, unless we have developed some additional skills, our brains can at times spend too much time imagining others' thought processes which could understandably affect feelings and then behaviours.

I work with many young people in schools who are in constant trouble due to negative mind reading. One young person was always in trouble for starting arguments and fights because of what she thought other people were thinking about her. When I taught her about mind reading, she recognised that she did it all the time. Once she had gained insight into what she did and began taking action to challenge it when it happened, her negative behaviour responses dropped significantly.

Fortune telling

This error in our thinking can lead children and young people to feel that they know what is going to happen in certain situations. This can lead to changes in attitude and behavioural choices, most often driven by fear or apprehension. In a nutshell, this is negative disaster planning which leads to expecting the worst and then causing the worst to actually happen (self-fulfilling prophecy).

It's important for parents, carers and teachers to notice changes in a child's behaviours and try and understand, or prompt them to communicate what the issue might be. If fortune telling is the case, we can then help children look for alternatives and evidence as to why this might not necessarily be the case.

Comparing

We all look and learn from others, that is how we keep evolving and developing. However, when this observational process becomes unbalanced, the results can affect feelings of positive well-being. Many children and young people can pay too much attention looking outwards at peers and social profiles which can lead to feelings of inferiority. From a very early age, children begin to assess who they are based on those around them. As adults, it is our role to have as many positive dialogues with children as possible, so that they can capture and store positive feelings about themselves inside. They learn to feel, love who they are and learn to cope more positively with this natural stage of development.

Catastrophising

Sometimes we can all be guilty of over dramatising and seeing a minor incident as a major disaster. The amount of time we spend overthinking after events can accelerate catastrophising. If children and young people are feeling sensitive to life events, catastrophising can sometimes take them over the edge of reality. Robbie did this a lot in 'The Blinks – Anger'. When he did things wrong, he immediately thought and believed everyone hated him or thought and believed that he was stupid, which fuelled feelings of failure and increased his angry reactions.

Top tips to reduce the impact of bias thinking patterns

- After your child or young person has experienced a difficult or intense feeling, talk to them. This helps them and you understand what they have just experienced and what they can do next time to make the situation better
- Listen actively to what your child is saying – they teach us!
- Explain that our brains are not always our friend and sometimes it can suggest things that might not be the best decision. This is normal and every brain does it at times. The trick is to sometimes question what our brain is asking us to do and why?

- If you feel that your child is engaged in an error thinking pattern, tell them about it so that they can see what they are doing, and the impact it is having on the choices that they are making

- Recognise these bias thinking patterns in yourself. If you think that your child is angry because you are a rubbish parent and they hate you, then you too will be more likely to react negatively. This could set negative examples and not offer the appropriate support to your child at that time

- Try little things that could make things better next time. Remember if we don't do anything differently, nothing will change!

Questions for discussion with children and young people.

1. Have you ever felt like Robbie did when his brain turned little incidents into much bigger disasters?

2. Have you ever found yourself:
   • Mind reading

   • Fortune telling

   • Comparing

   • Catastrophising

   How did this make you feel?

3. How could negative thinking patterns make us feel more angry?

4. Write down 5 things that you could say or do if your brain was not being your best friend with the choices that it was offering?

Section 3- How problematic anger impacts on Self-esteem

Our levels of self–esteem very much reflect how much we like and love ourselves. This self-love has a huge impact on what we feel we are capable of, what we perceive other people to think of us, and also how sensitive we are to rejection, mistakes and difficult life events. Robbie's problematic anger was beginning to have a damaging impact on his self-esteem, as he knew that the choices he made sometimes were not 'good'. This led him to feeling that he wasn't 'good' either.

We could argue that Robbie's self-esteem may have already been low due to difficult family relationships and Mum not being as emotionally available over the last few years since the death of Robbie's father. Children and young people with lower self-esteem can present with anger more readily, as it can be activated with feelings of failure or sadness. This sensitivity to feeling not good enough, clever enough, popular enough or any other 'enoughs' causes children to feel hurt more easily and so they are likely to express these intense negative feelings as angry outbursts.

Only too often, as we do as adults when our children are angry, hear only the angry words. It is essential that we learn to recognise all behaviour as a form of communication, so that we are able to provide what is needed at that time. We need to try and hear: 'I am hurt, I am frustrated, I am sad, I am insecure, I am vulnerable, I am scared,' etc.

This is also why healing chats after an emotional or behavioural incident are very important. If we do not engage with children and young people whilst they are calm, their thinking brain does not always get the opportunity to reflect and learn. We need to allow our children to feel whatever they are feeling no matter how difficult. However, they can only understand it through compassionate dialogue afterwards. When reparation chats don't happen, the angry or negative feelings can internalise feelings of badness which again can hinder positive self-esteem.

Talking together reconnects you with your child or young person and provides them with an outlet, so that intense feelings don't bottle up and explode in the future. Together we can help children accept anger and other negative emotions which, over time, allow children to cope with the wounds of life without reacting negatively. This leads children to make better choices, therefore becoming more emotionally intelligent. We don't need to be rocket scientists to see how making more balanced choices can lead to improved self-esteem, resilience and general well-being.

Questions & tasks for discussion with children and young people.

1. What do you like most about yourself? Write down as many things as you can until you run out.
2. How do you feel after a difficult day, or when you have been told off?
3. Think about the last time that you got angry. How did you feel afterwards?
4. Anger is the only emotion that doesn't exist on its own. Can you think of any other feelings that might have been there when you were angry?
5. What do you do when you feel difficult feelings like anger?
6. What don't you do now, that might help you feel better when you are angry next time?

Section 4 – Anger and Emotional Development

Human are governed by emotions, believed to be biologically activated, which continue to develop across the lifespan and which support further adaption and development. Emotions provide us with important information, can be highly motivational and are essential for individual progression and successful  relationships. However, if emotions are not accepted and nurtured, developmental problems can occur.

Emotional Development involves many cognitive and social processes including:

- recognising and managing emotions
- accurate decision-making
- developing care and compassion for oneself and others
- dealing with difficult situations effectively
- fostering positive relationships

As with many development issues, the early years can be seen to play a crucial role in future adaption. Studies looking at children's development over long periods of time suggest that the infant-caregiver relationships are where emotional development begins. It can be these key social factors such as parental sensitivity, intrusiveness, childhood social interaction, and mutual reciprocity which play an important part in emotional development. Therefore, the more emotionally aware we are as adults, the greater the opportunities for our children to learn from us, which enhances improved emotional development in our children.

Emotional development also has a part to play in supporting resilience in our children and young people. Resilience is thought to be a psychological and biological course which stems from the development of emotional learning, and again highly influenced by the quality of social interaction. The strength of these two crucial areas could dictate an individual's resilience, which is regarded to be the capability to deal with or overcome life's ups and downs.

In the Emotional Development Cycle by Levin (1982), we can see how emotional development occurs and the stages that children need to pass through successfully to progress as typically developing children. A simpler emotional development graph can be seen below:

Inappropriate Risk Taking Poor Relationships Not willing to separate	**SEPARATION & SEXUALITY**	Enjoys individuality & periods of independence Developing confidence sexual identity engage with new opportunities & challenges
Anti-authority & rules Mismatch expectations: skills Over casual; does not complete tasks	**STRUCTURE & SKILLS**	Enjoys diversity, difference, new skill Internal/external structure: Values, rules Identify same gender group
Threatening, bullying, lying Low self esteem, discounts Uses reputation to bolster self	**POWER & INDENTITY**	Positive sense of self; individual identity Different roles, relationships Understand consequences, contexts
Oppositional; acts tough Directs others; over-reacts Demanding, pushy; or victim	**THINKING**	Think, express & handle feelings Understand cause & effect, rules Think for themselves, say "No"
Passive, quiet, hangs back Unable to settle or focus Extreme responses	**DOING**	Curious, creative, take initiative Active, easily stimulated, seek sensory experiences Enjoy investigating, getting involved
Timid, withdrawn, fears change Out of touch with own needs, unable to voice needs Repetitive oral behaviours	**BEING**	Confidence & appropriately trusting Receptive to new experiences; open to relationships; willing to have a go Aware of needs; able to signal distress, ask for help, reach out

We can see how, as emotions begin to develop, we can see an appropriate response and guidance is required from us, the adults, at each phase. This helps to ensure that children gain knowledge and understanding from what they are feeling, and also what to do with those intense feelings, so that they do not impact negatively on development. A child who does not receive the correct information or understanding about difficult feelings, such as anger, during their early years could become emotionally stuck between the 'Doing' and 'Power and Identity' phases of emotional development, which happens a lot. If anger is modelled to children in a negative sense, or children are prevented from displaying anger, complications can set in.

As the active adults in our children's lives, it is important that we allow our children to feel whatever they are feeling, as this is part of growing up and learning. However, we must also educate our children when they are calmer and the rational, thinking brain has been reactivated. This will help them name what they were feeling and more importantly to know different ways of managing it next time it arises. It is this toolkit of things to try which most supports the emotional development and resilience of the children and young people that we care about.

Top tips to support healthy emotional development

- Nurture your children with love, guidance, patience, understanding and firm boundaries when needed
- Support your children with positive affirmations that allow them to be who they are
- Educate your children to name emotions and feelings
- Avoid talking to them when they are experiencing an intense emotion, as the thinking brain is not active and the words won't be received. Wait until they feel calmer and then talk about what happened, how it made them feel, and what could be done differently next time
- Try to use do's rather than don'ts
- Remember that young people will forget what you say but they will never forget how you made them feel.

Summary

This book has aimed to provide you with some relevant emotional and behavioural theory to help you gain a greater understanding of the psychology of anger. The more emotionally intelligent that we are about anger, the greater support we can provide to children who are struggling to understand this very intense feeling.

All children and young people get angry and so do adults. This is perfectly normal. We need to accept this before we can even think about regulating feelings of anger. By helping our children understand their feelings and learn from us whenever possible how to express them positively, our children can begin to develop in ways that are emotionally intelligent but which also supports positive well-being and resilience across the lifespan and future generations.

Anger - Summary Checklist – little things that can help in a big way!

- Breathe – anger is normal. How you react to and deal with their anger is what is important here. Stay calm and rational

- Young children or older children who are not emotionally progressing, do not have the developed brain pathways and circuits to be able to self-regulate so don't always see it as a choice or that they should know better

- Challenge any negative thinking patterns that could be driving angry feelings. Share with children the irrational thinking patterns from this book (mind reading, fortune telling, comparing & catastrophising) they are nothing to worry about, we all do it!

- Be empathetic to how difficult it must be for them when they are feeling so angry. Try and understand what other emotion might be present, e.g. hurt, fear, sadness and respond as you might if those emotions were being presented. This approach develops much stronger relationships

- When children and young people experience intense emotions, they are functioning with a primitive part of the brain which is trying to help them survive danger or threat. Talking will not help until they are calm

- Let them cry. This releases stress hormones that makes them feel better and also allows them to express the secondary emotion behind the anger. This is when the real healing can begin

- Acknowledge the feeling and provide alternatives such as: "I can see that you are really angry at the moment and that is ok, but I am not going to let you hurt yourself or anyone else. Try…"

Younger children:
- ✓ Stamping your feet
- ✓ Punching a pillow
- ✓ Ripping up or scrunching up pieces of paper
- ✓ Screaming loudly into a pillow
- ✓ Crying

Older children/young people - any of the above or:
- ✓ Squeezing ice tightly into their hands
- ✓ Bite into a lemon or lime – this will give them an intense sensation from anger
- ✓ Taking a walk or a run
- ✓ Trying to rip up a telephone directory
- ✓ Snapping an elastic band against their wrist
- ✓ Flattening aluminium cans

- Acknowledge the truth of what your child is feeling in that moment. This might involve you challenging your own thinking as to whether or not you think that they are doing it out of choice or as an over-reaction. The more compassionate you are, the more they will feel heard and supported and then the feelings will begin to shift

- Be safe. All children at times can push when they are feeling intense negative emo-tions like anger. If you can tolerate it, and stay calm and compassionate, then it is fine to allow. However if your child is hurting you then move away, and if need be, hold the wrist and explain that although they are feeling angry, you will not let them hurt you, as this is wrong and is more likely to make them feel sad afterwards. Again by remaining compassionate, children and young people are more likely to stop hitting, and cry instead

- Try not to overdo the emotional teaching part. Your child does know that what they did was wrong but didn't necessarily understand what it was, or how to do things differently next time. The more you help them understand angry feelings, the more likely they will learn what to do with them more positively over time

If you and your child have enjoyed 'The Blinks – Anger' novel (Book 2 in this series) then look out for 'The Blinks – Worry' (Book 1). Keep an eye out for Book 3 'The Blinks – Self-Esteem', due for release Spring 2016.

To get in touch on social media, please go to:

Facebook - /Theblinksbooks

Twitter - @BlinksThe

OTHER TITLES IN THE SERIES:

'The Blinks' – Worry

'A magical novel for 7-11-year-olds'.

'The Blinks' are created from morsels of goodness, that all the good folk who have ever lived leave to the Universe. Their whole purpose is to share their wisdom and kindness with children.

When Amanda is discussed at the midnight meeting, she is lucky to become part of some very special Blink intervention. As a result Amanda begins to make changes, she never thought possible.

'The Blinks' Worry – A Reference Manual for Parents, Carers & Teachers

All 'The Blinks' books have been created to help children, young people and their families understand emotional and behavioural issues. More so, they provide strategies and techniques to help manage and change the intensity and duration of problematic behaviours over time.

This supportive booklet accompanies the book "The Blinks' – Worry' written specifically for older children and those in their early teens. It provides a deeper understanding of the psychology of worry and anxiety for parents, carers and teachers, and how anger can impact on other developmental issues. It also provides lots of 'top tips' on what works best for children and young people whilst growing up and some activity questions that can be used as a starting point to initiate emotive dialogue or discussion with children.

'The Blinks' - Anger

Robbie's life has never been great, but the events over the last few years have slowly made him more and more unhappy and angry. One day it all gets too much and his anger erupts!

A sequence of wrong choices leaves Robbie with a string of problems that need sorting out. Luckily Chika Change-Your-Thoughts sees that he needs help at this difficult time. Together with Cale, 'the community bad lad with a heart', Robbie learns just who is responsible for his anger and how to deal with it.

To order any of the above books go to: www.theblinks.co.uk

To find out more and become a 'fan' of Andrea Chatten and 'The Blinks' go to:

www.oodlebooks.com

Also available on Amazon & Kindle.